Islamic Quiz
Book 2

Dr. Jamal-un-Nisa Siddiqui
Dr. Abia Afsar-Siddiqui

Reprinted 1984, 1986, 1990, 1996, 1998, 2002
Revised January 2006
Reprint : 2009

Published by:
Ta-Ha Publishers Ltd.
Unit 4, The Windsor Centre
Windsor Grove
West Norwood
LONDON SE27 9NT

Website: http://www.taha.co.uk
Email: sales@taha.co.uk

Written by: Dr. Jamal-un-Nisa Siddiqui
& Dr. Abia Afsar-Siddiqui
Cover Design: Mariama Janneh

A catalogue record of this book is available from the British Library.

ISBN 1 842000 73 X

Printed and bound by: De-Luxe Printers, London NW10 7NR

Introduction

This second quiz book follows the success, alhamdulillah, of IQ1. The questions have largely been taken from the Qur'an and hadith and references have been given with the answers as far as possible. It is hoped that the reader will use this quiz book as a starting point to learn more about the Qur'an and Islamic historical events.

As with IQ1, this book contains 5 quizzes of 20 questions each on general knowledge about Islam. For each 20 question quiz: scores over 10 are good; scores over 15 are excellent; scores over 17 are outstanding. The answers are given in sequence from page 18.

The following abbreviations have been used throughout the book:

(SWT) should be read as *subhanahu wa ta'ala*
(SAAS) should be read as *sallalahu alaihi wa sallam*
(AS) should be read as *alaihi salam* (male)
                              alaiha salam (female)
(RA) should be read as *radhiallahu anhu*
BC means Before Christ when referring to a date.

Drs. J.U.N Siddiqui and A. Afsar-Siddiqui
London
Dhul-Hijjah 1426 AH
January 2006 CE

QUIZ 1

1. What does the Arabic word Islam mean?

2. Which unique book provides mankind with Divine Guidance according to the laws of Islam?

3. What is the Arabic name for Islamic Law?

4. One of the basic sources of Islamic Law is the Qur'an. What is the other one?

5. Who refused to bow down to Adam (AS) when ordered to do so by Allah (SWT)?

6. What are the names of the two sons of Adam (AS)?

7. In which country was Prophet Nuh (AS) sent to preach the Right Way of Allah (SWT)?

8. How many years did Prophet Nuh (AS) preach the Right Way to his nation before The Great Flood?

9. What was the name of the nation to whom Prophet Hud (AS) was sent? They were an Arabian tribe who lived in *Ahqaf*, a place surrounded by Hijaz, Yemen and Yamamah.

10. What is the name of the nation to whom Prophet Salih (AS) was sent? These people lived in an area now in Jordan. The fifteenth surah of the Qur'an is named after their capital city which was *Al-Hijr*.

11. The people of Salih (AS) demanded a clear sign or miracle as proof that he was a Messenger of Allah. What did Prophet Salih (AS) present them with?

12. Where was Prophet Ibrahim (AS) born?

13. Who was king of Iraq at the time of Ibrahim (AS)?

14. What was the name and occupation of Ibrahim (AS)'s father?

15. Prophet Ibrahim (AS) had a son named Ishaq by his first wife, Sarah and another named Isma'il by his second wife, Hajrah. What were the names of his third wife and their son?

16. Which two nations sprang from the first two sons of Ibrahim (AS)?

17. Give the name of Prophet Ibrahim (AS)'s nephew who migrated to the Jordanian city of *Sadum* to invite people to Islam?

18. When the people of Prophet Lut (AS) rejected his message, how were they punished by Allah?

19. What was the name of Prophet Yusuf (AS)'s younger brother?

20. The people of Midian were also called the people of *Al-Aikah*. They associated partners with Allah and were dishonest in trade. Which prophet was sent to guide them?

QUIZ 2

1. What was the name of the pharaoh who ruled over Egypt when Musa (AS) was born and what was the name of his wife?

2. Which pharaoh did Musa (AS) invite to accept the Divine Message of Allah and set the Bani Isra'il free from their slavery?

3. There were a total of nine signs or miracles that were sent by Allah (SWT) to Prophet Musa (AS). Name at least four of these.

4. Give the name of the prophet that was appointed by Allah (SWT) as an assistant to Musa (AS) when he asked for a helper.

5. Where was Prophet Musa (AS) summoned by Divine Command so that the Divine Law could be given to him and how long did he stay there?

6. While Prophet Musa (AS) was receiving the Divine Law, what did his people do in his absence?

7. What is the name of the food sent down by Allah to Bani Isra'il in the Sinai desert for forty years?

8. Give the name of the ancestral clan of Prophets Musa and Harun (AS) which was assigned to look after the twelve clans of Israel, comprising ten sons of Yaqub (AS) and two sons of Yusuf (AS).

9. The Levites inherited a 'box' from the family of Musa and Harun (AS), which is called the Ark of the Covenant. By what name is the Ark of the Covenant mentioned in the Qur'an?

10. The Ark of the Covenant contained four holy articles. Three of these were: a) the tablets containing commandments that were given to Prophet Musa (AS) on Mount Tur by Allah (SWT); b) the original copy of the Torah; c) a bottle containing Manna. What was the fourth article in the 'box'?

11. After Prophet Musa (AS), the chiefs of Bani Isra'il asked their Prophet for a king who would fight the enemy and get back the Ark of the Covenant which they had lost. What was the name of the king that Allah (SWT) appointed?

12. Talut, the king of Bani Isra'il, fought with Jalut (Goliath) and his army. Who was the young man that finally killed Jalut?

13. To whom did Allah (SWT) grant Prophethood and a book called the *Zabur*?

14. What was the name of the Queen of Saba whom Sulayman (AS) invited to visit him and who subsequently accepted Islam and became Sulayman (AS)'s wife?

15. How were the Prophets Ilyas and Al-Yasa' (AS) related to each other?

16. Which prophet was sent to Ninevah (now in Iraq) about 800 years BC for the guidance of the Assyrians?

17. The cousin of Isa (AS), known to the Christians as John the Baptist, was beheaded on the order of King Herod merely to please one of the dancers in his court. By what name is this prophet referred to in the Qur'an?

18. The mother of Isa (AS) was Maryam (AS). What were the names of Maryam (AS)'s father and mother?

19. For how long did Prophet Isa (AS) preach the Word of Allah to his people?

20. Put the following prophets in order of when they came, with the earliest first:
    a) Yusuf (AS)   b) Yaqub (AS)
    c) Ishaq (AS)   d) Dawud (AS)
    e) Sulayman (AS)   f) Isa (AS)
    g) Yahya (AS)   h) Musa (AS)

QUIZ 3

1. The Prophet Muhammad (SAAS) was descended from which son of Ibrahim (AS)?

2. After Prophet Ibrahim (AS) re-built the Ka'bah with his son, Isma'il (AS), how many more times was the Ka'bah re-built?

3. When the Prophet (SAAS) migrated to Madinah from Makkah, where did he stay for the first three days? (Hint: the first mosque of the Islamic Era was then built there.)

4. What was the name of the Prophet (SAAS)'s she-camel upon which he migrated to Madinah?

5. When the command came to change the direction of the Qibla (in 1st Hijri), the Prophet (SAAS) was leading the Dhuhr or Asr salah at Madinah facing Masjid al-Aqsa. Through what angle did the worshippers have to turn in order to face Makkah?

6. On what occasion was the following prayer said by the Prophet Muhammad (SAAS): "O Allah, here are the Quraysh proud of their war material. They have come to prove that your Messenger is false. O Allah, now send the help that you have promised to send me. O Allah, if this little army of your slaves is destroyed, there will be no-one left in the land to worship you."?

7. In the Battle of Uhud, the Prophet (SAAS) led an army of one thousand men to meet the enemy, but the ringleader of the hypocrites, Abdullah bin Ubayy, deserted him with his three hundred men. Seventy Muslims were martyred and many injured, including the Prophet. According to the Islamic calendar when was this battle fought?

8. In the fifth year of Hijrah, the Jews joined ranks with the Arabs to form a large army to defeat Islam. The Muslims dug a trench around Madinah to defend themselves. What was the name of the battle?

9. In the sixth year of Hijrah, the Makkans tried to prevent 1400 Muslims from performing 'Umrah for the first time since the migration to Madinah. One of the Prophet's Companions was sent to talk to the Unbelievers of Makkah. Who was it?

10. In the sixth year of Hijrah, the Prophet (SAAS) signed a peace treaty with the Makkans which prevented both sides from fighting for 10 years. What was this peace treaty called?

11. Which surah of the Qur'an gives details of the Treaty of Hudaybiyah?

12. At Hudaydiyah, the Muslims took an oath of allegiance to the Prophet (SAAS) that they would stand by him and obey Allah and His Prophet. What is this oath called?

13. After the peace treaty of Hudaybiyah, the Prophet Muhammad (SAAS) sent letters to leaders of other countries inviting them to accept Islam. They were Emperor Heraclius of Syria, Shah Chosroes of Persia, King Negus of Abyssinia, and Muwaqis of Egypt. Only one of these leaders accepted the Prophet (SAAS)'s call to Islam. Which leader was it?

14. After the conquest of Makkah, the first Hajj of the Islamic period was performed in eighth Hijri according to the old customs. The second Hajj was performed in ninth Hijri by Muslims according to the Islamic way and non-Muslims according to their own way. Did the Prophet Muhammad (SAAS) perform either of these two Hajj?

15. In the ninth year of Hijrah, to where did the Prophet (SAAS) lead an expedition of 30,000 men to fight the Romans?

16. What is the name given to the third Hajj which was performed in the tenth year of Hijrah only by Muslims according to the Islamic way under the guidance of the Prophet Muhammad (SAAS)?

17. When the Companions of the Prophet (SAAS) used to meet, which surah of the Qur'an would they recite to each other before parting company?

18. What is the name given to about three to four hundred of the Prophet (SAAS)' s companions who spent most of their time in his company, acquiring knowledge and dedicating themselves to Islam?

19. About which surah did the Prophet (SAAS) say, "This has been revealed to me as an indication that my task is over in this world and I shall soon see my Lord."?

20. In which month and year of the Islamic calendar did the Prophet (SAAS) pass away?

QUIZ 4

1. How many times is the Prophet Muhammad (SAAS) mentioned in the Qur'an **by name**?

2. In the Qur'an the Jews are generally referred to as Bani Isra'il, but in some places the Qur'an calls them by another name. What is that name?

3. By what name are the Christians referred to in the Qur'an?

4. What were the names of the two angels appointed by Allah who came to the people of Babylon in human form to teach them Black Magic as a test?

5. How many ayat of the Qur'an require the reader to do *sajdah* when they are being recited?

6. Surah al-Hijr, ayah 87 says, "We have given you seven much repeated verses..." According to the majority of scholars and authentic hadith, which surah is being referred to here?

7. Which ayat of the Qur'an did Prophet Muhammad (SAAS) teach to the children of his family to help give them understand about the Oneness of Allah?

8. Which surah and ayah contains complete and detailed orders for wearing hijab for Muslim women and in which Islamic year was this surah revealed?

9. Which of the Qur'anic surahs is named after one of the uncles of the Prophet (SAAS)? He and his wife were bitter enemies of Islam.

10. The Prophet (SAAS) said, "Whoever wants to know about the Day of Judgement as if he had seen it with his own eyes should read these three surahs." To which three surahs was he referring?

11. How many times is the creation of Adam (AS) mentioned in the Qur'an?

12. Which is the longest surah of the Qur'an revealed in one go?

13. Under which Khalifah were the dots and vowel marks placed in the Qur'an?

14. What is the name given to those who memorise the whole of the Qur'an?

15. Can you name the first five surahs of the Qur'an?

16. Give the names of the last five surahs of the Qur'an.

17. How many surahs of the Qur'an are named after a Prophet and do you know which ones they are?

18. Seven surahs of the Qur'an have more than one name. Can you name at least two such surahs and give the alternative name as well?

19. Which two prophets are each mentioned only twice by name in the Qur'an?

20. Which surah of the Qur'an is named after the mother of a prophet?

QUIZ 5

1. What is *Kalima Tayyiba*?

2. How many daily salah was the Prophet Muhammad (SAAS) first given during his Ascension to Heaven (*Mi'raj*)?

3. Who, according to the Prophet (SAAS), told him to go back to Allah and ask for the daily salah to be reduced in number?

4. What is the name given to the act of raising the hands to the ears and lowering them while saying *Allahu Akbar* at the beginning of salah?

5. According to hadith, salah in congregation is how many more times more rewarding than salah performed alone?

6. According to hadith, what will happen to the parts of the body that have been washed during wudu on the Day of Judgement?

7. What is the literal meaning of the word Zakat, the third pillar (*rukun*) of Islam?

8. According to the Qur'an there are eight categories of people who can receive Zakat. Six of these are: a) the poor; b) the needy; c) Zakat collectors; d) converts to Islam; e) people who are not free; f) those in debt. What are the remaining two categories of people who are eligible to receive Zakat?

9. In which Islamic year did it become obligatory for Muslims to pay Zakat?

10. What is the name given to the amount that every Muslim must give at the end of Ramadan but before Eid salah?

11. In which surah of the Qur'an does Allah give the main instruction about Ramadan?

12. Which month of the Islamic calendar is Ramadan and what does the word Ramadan mean?

13. What is the name of the pre-dawn meal that it is recommended to eat before starting the fast?

14. The word *sawm* is used in Arabic for fasting, but what does the word *sawm* literally mean?

15. Which night according to the Qur'an is said to be better than one thousand months and when it is said to be?

16. In preparing to perform Hajj or 'Umrah, all pilgrims put on special clothes. What are these called in Arabic?

17. During Hajj, all Muslims run between two hills near Ka'bah. What are the names of these two hills?

18. Circling around the Ka'bah seven times in an anticlockwise direction is called *Tawaf*. What name is given to the act of running between the hills of Safa and Marwah?

19. In which surah and ayah of the Qur'an does it state that Hajj has been made compulsory for all those who can afford it?

20. During Hajj, every Haji must offer an animal for sacrifice in order to be released from *Ihram*. Where and on which date of the Islamic Calendar is this done?

Answers

Quiz 1

1. To submit or surrender to the will of Allah

2. Qur'an al-Karim

3. Shari'ah

4. Sunnah (example of the Prophet (SAAS))

5. Iblis (2:34)

6. Habil and Qabil

7. Iraq

8. 950 years (29:14)

9. The nation of A'ad

10. The nation of Thamud

11. A she-camel (7:73)

12. In Ur, northern Iraq in about 2100BC

13. Namrud or Nimrod

14. Azar (6:74) who was a sculptor

15. Qaturah and Midian. It was from Midian that the Prophet Shu'aib (AS) was descended.

16. Ismailites and Israelites

17. Prophet Lut (AS)

18. Stones rained down from the sky (7:84)

19. Bin Yamin

20. Prophet Shu'aib (AS)

Quiz 2

1. Rameses II and his wife was Asiya

2. Mineptah

3. Musa (AS)'s staff turned into a serpent (20:20); his hand shone brightly (20:22); drought (7:130); loss of fruits (7:130); flood (7:133); locusts (7:133); lice (7:133); frogs (7:133); blood (7:133)

4. Harun (AS) who was Musa (AS)'s elder brother

5. Mount Tur or Mount Sinai for forty days

6. They started worshipping a golden calf

7. Manna and Salwa

8. The Levites

9. Tabut-e-Sakina (2:248)

10. The staff of Prophet Musa (AS)

11. Talut (2:247)

12. Dawud (AS) (2:251)

13. Dawud (AS) (4:163)

14. Bilqis (She is not named in the Qur'an but her name is given in Tafsir ibn Kathir and Tafsir Qurtubi)

15. They were cousins. Prophet Ilyas was descended from Harun (AS).

16. Yunus (AS)

17. Yahya (AS)

18. Imran and Hannah (Imran is mentioned in the Qur'an and the Tafsirs of ibn Kathir and Qurtubi mention Hannah who was the daughter of Faqood)

19. Three years

20. Ishaq (AS); Yaqub (AS); Yusuf (AS); Musa (AS); Dawud (AS); Sulayman (AS); Yahya (AS); Isa (AS)

Quiz 3

1. Isma'il (AS)

2. Seven times (By 1. Bani Jerham; 2. Amalqa; 3. Qasi bin Kalaab; 4. Quraysh (the Prophet (SAAS) also participated); 5. Abdullah bin Zubayr (RA); 6. Hajaj bin Yusuf; 7. Sultan Murad Khan Usmani)

3. Quba, a place at the entrance of Madinah

4. Qaswa

5. 180 degrees

6. Battle of Badr

7. Shawwal, in the third year of Hijrah

8. Battle of the Trench or *Khandaq*

9. Usman (RA)

10. The Treaty of Hudaybiyah

11. Surah al-Fatah (48)

12. The Oath of Ridwan

13. Negus (or Najashi) of Abyssinia

14. No

15. Tabuk

16. *Hajjatul Wida*

17. Surah al-'Asr (Surah 103)

18. *Ashab as-Saffah*

19. Surah an-Nasr (Surah 110)

20. In Rabi al-Awwal of the eleventh year of Hijrah

Quiz 4

1. Four times (3:144; 33:40; 47:2; 48:29)

2. *Hadu* or *Yahud*

3. *Nasarah*

4. Harut and Marut (2:102)

5. Fourteen

6. Surah al-Fatihah (Surah 1)

7. Surah al-Furqan (25) ayat 2

8. Surah an-Nur ayah 31 in the fifth year of Hijrah

9. Surah al-Lahab (Surah 111)

10. Surahs Takweer (81), Infitar (82) and Inshiqaq (84)

11. Seven times (2:30-38; 7:11-25; 15:28-39; 17:61-63; 18:50; 20:116-123; 38:71-76)

12. Surah al-Anam (Surah 6)

13. Usman (RA)

14. Hafiz

15. al-Fatihah, al-Baqarah, 'Al-'Imran, an-Nisa, al-Ma'idah

16. an-Nasr, al-Lahab, al-Ikhlas, al-Falaq, an-Nas

17. Six surahs: Surahs Yunus (10), Hud (11), Yusuf (12), Ibrahim (14), Muhammad (47), Nuh (71).

18. Tawbah or Bara'ah (Surah 9)
    Isra or Bani Isra'il (Surah 17)
    Ghafir or Mu'min (Surah 40)
    Fussilat or Ham Meem Sajdah (Surah 41)
    Qalam or Nun (Surah 68)
    Ad-Dahr or Al-Insan (Surah 76)
    Lahab or Masad or Tabbat (Surah 111)

19. Prophets Ilyas and Al-Yasa' (AS)

20. Surah Maryam (19)

Quiz 5

1. *La illaha illalah Muhammadur Rasulullah*

2. Fifty

3. Prophet Musa (AS)

4. *Takbir al-Tehrima*

5. 27 (Bukhari and Muslim)

6. They will shine (Muslim and Bukhari)

7. Purification

8. In the Way of Allah and travellers (9:60)

9. In the second year of Hijrah

10. *Zakat al-Fitr*

11. Surah al-Baqarah ayat 182-186

12. Ramadan is the ninth month and literally means 'scorching heat'.

13. *Suhur*

14. To refrain from

15. *Laylat ul-Qadr* found in one of the odd nights in the last ten nights of Ramadan.

16. *Ihram*

17. Safa and Marwah (2:157)

18. *Sa'ee*

19. Surah Al-'Imran (3) ayah 97

20. Mina on 10th Dhul Hijjah